PHONICS IN CONTEXT

Written by Bev Heaton

World Teachers Press

Published with the permission of R.I.C. Publications Pty. Ltd.

Copyright © 1997 by Didax, Inc., Rowley, MA 01969. All rights reserved.

First published by R.I.C. Publications Pty. Ltd., Perth, Western Australia.

Printed in the United States of America.

Order Number 2-5036
ISBN 1-885111-49-5

C D E F   98 99

Educational Resources

395 Main Street
Rowley, MA 01969

Introduction

In *Phonics In Context*, each phonic sound is introduced in context, allowing students to identify the specific sound within text. Thus, students will be able to process automatically each phonic sound for pronunciation and meaning, thereby enhancing their reading and spelling skills. The activities in the book also provide reinforcement of each sound, and the comprehension stories which follow enable the students to identify the sounds in context.

Contents

Teacher Information

Introduction

The teaching of basic sounds has long been recognized as an important component when learning the English language. This series of books looks at introducing the digraph sounds that form the foundation of this learning, through a variety of interesting and fun activities which students will enjoy. In addition, the author has provided activities that include the specific digraph sound in the context of a short story. This 'learning in context' is a vital part of learning and is a feature of this series. The activities are the product of many years of practice and application by the author and represent a wealth of experience.

What is a digraph?

A digraph is formed when a pair of letters make a single sound, such as *ew* in *stew* or *th* in *thief.*

It is important to teach digraphs and trigraphs as part of a language program. It provides students with a background in graphophonics and enables them to recognize letter patterns in their reading, writing and oral language.

As an extension, it is also important to teach that some letter combinations form different sound patterns in different situations such as *th* in *thief* and *th* in *then.* It is also necessary to teach students that the same sounds can be formed using different letter combinations such as, *ar* in *jar* and *au* in *aunt.*

Development

Below are two activities which could also be incorporated to develop the children's awareness of visual patterns and letter combinations.

1. Ask students to make pairs of words that rhyme, e.g. mouse/house. This could be developed further as a game of *Snap* or *Patience.*

2. Use the game *Hangman* with an alternative rule. The students must give you letters of the word in the correct order. The letters selected by the students will fit into three areas.

   (i) Could be - these are letter combinations that belong together (e.g. ye).

   (ii) Couldn't be - these are letter combinations that don't belong together (e.g. yt).

   (iii) The letter is the next letter in the word and is placed as part of the secret word.

Teacher Information - example lesson development

The following is a lesson development using one of the pages in this book. It is an example of how the activity could be introduced, developed and extended.

Activity

'ow' as in grow - pages 6 & 7

Introductory Work

Introducing a sound can be done in a variety of ways. However the two most important parts of the introduction should be first, to identify places or words where the sound can be found. This then gives the students a logical reason to learn the sound and hence the words containing this sound. Secondly, the correct pronunciation of the sound is important so that different sounds can be easily distinguished. Students can contribute to both of these areas and a large group activity suits these items well.

Pictures representing words containing the 'ow' sound will assist with the introduction.

Development

The first worksheet identifies the sound and allows the students to practice using the sound to make different words, using pictorial clues. The second worksheet provides a passage of writing which includes a quantity of 'ee' words. This will allow the students to work the 'ee' words in context and gain a greater level of understanding.

1. First activity provides practice in creating 'ow' words by placing the 'ow' sound. Students should verbalize their answers wherever possible.

2. Locating 'ow' words from given clues. Students have the base sound and need to match it with initial sounds to produce the word.

3. Follow up by identifying more 'ee' words and writing them on the board for students to practice.

Note: activities in this book will become progressively harder and students should be encouraged to complete items independently before discussing answers.

1. Read the story individually and as a class, with students following the words. Talk about what happened in the story.

2. Discuss the questions and then have students write their answers. Discuss.

3. Questions that ask for opinions as well as fact should be discussed and students should explain their answers.

Extension

Further use of digraph sounds and words containing these sounds should become part of the daily language program. Where words containing these sounds are located they should be identified and discussed to further emphasize the sound in the context of the student's daily contact with written language. Use of appropriate words in students' writing should be encouraged so that word banks are developed.

'ow' as in grow

Print the missing 'ow' sound.

cr_ _   s_ _

gl_ _   m_ _   l_ _

burr_ _   shad_ _

sparr_ _   yell_ _

What am I? Draw me.

I have wings. I can fly. I am little.
What am I?_____

I am black. I have a sharp beak.
What am I?_____

I am always with you. I am on
the floor, the wall, the door.
What am I?_____

Read the story.
Underline all the words with 'ow' sounds.

One day Joe Crow and Jill Sparrow flew down out of their willow tree to visit Ronny Rabbit, who lived in a burrow. They flew low over the burrow in the glow of the sunlight. As they passed over the burrow, they could see their shadows. Ronny Rabbit popped his head out of his burrow and said, 'Good morning Joe Crow and Jill Sparrow.' 'Good morning,' answered Joe Crow and Jill Sparrow, 'You really have grown into a beautiful rabbit. May we come in for a cup of morning tea?' 'Yes, of course,' said Ronny Rabbit. So they all went into the burrow for morning tea.

Answer these questions.

Who flew out of the willow tree?

_____

What time of the day was it?

_____

Why do you think Joe Crow and Jill Sparrow wanted to visit Ronny Rabbit?

_____

Do you think Ronny Rabbit was lonely?_____

Why?_____

'aw' as in claw

Print the missing 'aw' sound.
Match the word to the picture.

f__ __n

cr__ __l

h__ __k

cl__ __

y__ __n

pr__ __n

str__ __

Print the missing words.

I can drink through a _____.

A baby _____s when she is tired.

A _____ is a baby deer.

A _____ has sharp _____s.

Read the story.
Circle all the words with 'aw' sounds.

I saw a hawk with sharp claws. The hawk flew low over the lawn where a fawn was eating some straw. The fawn saw the hawk and crawled away so the hawk could not get her. She hurt her jaw on the lawn as she crawled. The fawn waited until the hawk flew away. She started to yawn so she laid dow the lawn and went to sleep.

Answer these questions.

What did the hawk have?

_____

Where did the hawk fly?

_____

What did the fawn see?

_____

How do you think the fawn felt?

_____

Why did the fawn start to yawn?

_____

'ew' as in stew

Finish the words.
Draw a picture for each word.

scr___ ___

thr___ ___

j___ ___el

ch___ ___

cr___ ___

dr___ ___

Print the missing words.

The captain and his _____ sailed on a big ship.

I _____ the ball and the dog caught it and

_____ed it.

My teacher _____ on the chalkboard.

Dad put a _____ in the door with a

_____ driver.

Read the story.
Underline all the words with 'ew' sounds.

Simon Hew cooked a stew for the crew on a big boat. The crew said the stew was delicious. The meat was tender so the crew was able to chew it. Simon Hew drew a picture of the crew chewing the stew. The crew gave Simon Hew a jewel for making the stew.
Simon Hew threw the jewel into the sea.

Answer these questions.

What was the cook's name?

_____

Did the crew like the stew?

_____

What did Simon Hew draw a picture of?

_____

Why did the crew give Simon the jewel?

_____

Why do you think Simon threw the jewel?

_____

How many 'ew' words did you find? _____

'u-e' as in flute

Finish the words.
Draw a picture for each word.

m__l__

t__b__

fl__t__

r__l__r

pr__n__

Print the missing words.

mute   mule   A _____ is an animal.

tune   tube   I can play a _____ on the tuba.

mute   tube   Toothpaste comes in a _____.

use   cute   A puppy is very _____.

Phonics In Context   *World Teachers Press*

Read the story.
Circle all the words with 'u-e' sounds.

June had a pet mule and a cute puppy. The mule could carry a load on his back. June and her puppy would walk alongside the mule as they went for a long walk. As they walked, June would play a tune on her recorder. The cute little puppy loved to hear June play the recorder. His tail would wag as he walked. The mule would nod his head up and down. June would give a cube of sugar to the mule and a prune to the puppy. June's pets loved her.

Answer these questions.

What pets did June have?

_____

Could the mule carry a load?

_____

What would June play a tune on?

_____

What would June give her pets?

_____

Why do you think June's pets loved her?

_____

'oi' as in oil
Finish the words.
Draw a picture for each word.

s__ __l

t__ __l

__ __l

f__ __l

c__ __n

b__ __l

Print the missing words.

point   **joint**

A dart has a sharp _____.

spoil   **oil**

Cars need _____ to make them run well.

foil   **soil**

Plants will grow in _____.

join   **coin**

The tooth fairy left me a ten cent _____.

Read the story.
Circle all the words with 'oi' sounds.

Damien was a very spoiled little boy. He had a toy train. The train needed oil to run well. One day Damien got three more train cars so he joined them together with a coil. It made a lot of noise. Damien put more oil in the joints and the noise stopped. The train came off the tracks into some soil. The soil spoiled the joints. Damien cleaned the joints and put more oil on them. The train was not spoiled any more.

Answer these questions.

What was Damien?

_____

What did the train need?

_____

What did Damien use to join the train cars?

_____

Why did the joints get spoiled?

_____

Do you think Damien liked his train?

_____

Why?_____

'ear' as in fear

Finish the words.
Draw a picture for each word.

t_ _ _

h_ _ _

f_ _ _

sp_ _ _ _

_ _ _ _s

n_ _ _ _

Rewrite these words.
Add 'ear' to these letters.

h _____

sp _____

t _____

disapp _____

app _____

n _____

Read the story.
Underline all the words with 'ear' sounds.

Years ago a thirty-year-old woman went for a walk in the forest. She disappeared for a long time. Some people went searching for her. They came near her, but they could not hear her cries for help. As she cried, the tears ran down her cheeks. She made a spear out of a long branch from a tree. With the spear she could help herself stand up. The woman had to be careful because there was a sheer drop just beside her. She stood up and hobbled out of the forest. The searchers saw her appear from out of the forest. They were happy to see her.
They had tears in their eyes.

Answer these questions.

How old was the woman?

_____

Where did she disappear?

_____

Was the woman upset?

_____

Why were the searchers happy?

_____

'air' as in hair

Finish the words.
Draw a picture for each word.

st_ _ _ ☐

p_ _ _ ☐

l_ _ _ ☐

f_ _ _y ☐

ch_ _ _ ☐

f_ _ _ ☐

h_ _ _ ☐

Answer 'Yes' or 'No'.

Can you climb stairs?_____

Does a lion live in a lair?_____

Do you have a pair of gloves?_____

Can you sit on a chair?_____

Phonics In Context *World Teachers Press*

Read the story.
Underline all the words with 'air' sounds.

Lippy Lion lived all alone in his lair. He was very sad. One day he lay in the entrance of his lair. He was dreaming about how he would love to have a friend. Suddenly, out of nowhere a little fairy appeared. She had beautiful hair. The fairy asked the lion, 'Would you like to come to the fair with me?' 'Oh, yes, please,' answered the lion. So off to the fair went Lippy and the little fairy. After the fair was over, they went back to Lippy's lair. Lippy said, 'Thank you little fairy.' Little fairy said goodbye to Lippy and flew away.

Answer these questions.

Where did Lippy live?

_____

Why was he sad?

_____

_____

Who did Lippy go to the fair with?

_____

Do you think Lippy was happy?_____

Why?_____

_____

'ought' as in fought

**Print the missing 'ought' sound.
Then write each word.**

th__ __ __ __ __   _____

br__ __ __ __ __   _____

b__ __ __ __ __   _____

s__ __ __ __ __   _____

f__ __ __ __ __   _____

Put in the missing words.

I _____ my new bike to school to show the
  (bought/brought)

other students.

My mother _____ me some new clothes.
            (bought/brought)

The savage dog _____ the dog for the bone.
                (sought/fought)

Use this word in a sentence.

thoughtful

_____

Phonics In Context   *World Teachers Press*

Read the story.
Underline all the words with 'ought' sounds.

David went to the store for his mother. He thought his mother asked him to buy some groceries. Among these groceries were milk, sugar, eggs and cold meat. He bought these groceries and brought them home in a bag hanging from the handlebars of his bike. He thought he had bought everything his mother had asked for, but he hadn't. He had forgotten the milk. As he rode his bike back to the store a dog chased him. He fought the dog off and continued on his way. David bought the milk and returned home. He brought the milk inside and put it on the table in the kitchen.
His mother was grateful.

Answer these questions.

What groceries did David buy?

_____

What did David forget? _____

How do you think David felt when he forgot the milk?

_____

Why do you think the dog chased David?

_____

Why was David's mother grateful?

_____

'au' as in sauce

Print the missing 'au' sound.

c _ _ se   l _ _ nched

h _ _ nted   l _ _ ndry

s _ _ ce   _ _ tumn

astron _ _ t   h _ _ l

P _ _ l   _ _ gust

Choose from the above words to fill the blanks.

The ghost _____ the house.

Tomato _____ tastes delicious on pasta.

In _____ the spaceship will be _____ into space.

The _____ leaves made the _____ on the line dirty.

Read and draw.

Paul and Paula inside a haunted house eating from a saucer.

Read the story.
Circle all the words with 'au' sounds.

Paul and Paula were both astronauts. They were going to be launched into space on August fourth. It would not be autumn but that didn't matter. Paul and Paula were going to haul a load of laundry with them and a huge saucer to detect radio waves. From mission control the astronauts can receive messages. These messages are then sent back to earth through the use of the larger saucer. As the launching date grew nearer, Paul and Paula, the two astronauts, began to get excited. They did not want to haul a load of laundry but they did want to haul the large saucer and place it in space, so they could send and receive messages.

Answer these questions.

What were Paul and Paula?

_____

Which season does August fall in?

_____

Why did Paul and Paula want to haul the saucer?

_____

Why didn't Paul and Paula want to haul the laundry?

_____

Why do you think the astronauts were excited?

_____

'ur' as in picture

Print the missing 'ur' sound.

fut __ __ e   creat __ __ e

advent __ __ e   capt __ __ e

furnit __ __ e   fract __ __ e

punct __ __ e   nat __ __ e

pict __ __ e

Answer 'Yes' or 'No'.

Can you build furniture? _____

Are you scared of creepy creatures? _____

Have you been on an adventure? _____

Have you ever captured a tiger? _____

Write a sentence for the words:

picture, puncture, future

_____

_____

Read the story.
Circle all the words with 'ur' sounds.

A furry creature lived among some very old furniture. It was always frightened it might get captured. It was a creature of nature and it was always looking for adventure. In the very near future the furry creature was to have an adventure it would never forget. It would be captured and kept locked up in a cage hidden behind a picture. One night the furry creature peeped from behind the old furniture where it lived to see if it was safe to come out and explore. Nothing was in sight, so the furry creature crept out. Soon a huge human creature spotted him, grabbed him and locked him in a cage.

Answer these questions.

Why was the furry creature frightened?

_____

What is meant by 'a creature of nature'?

_____

What is meant by 'future'?

_____

How do you think the creature felt when he was captured?

_____

What do you think happened?

_____

_____

'tion' as in reflection

Print the missing 'tion' sound.

fric___ ___ ___ ___

invita___ ___ ___ ___

planta___ ___ ___ ___

direc___ ___ ___ ___

subtrac___ ___ ___ ___

collec___ ___ ___ ___

posi___ ___ ___ ___

fac___ ___ ___ ___

sta___ ___ ___ ___

reflec___ ___ ___ ___

ac___ ___ ___ ___

sec___ ___ ___ ___

What is the meaning of: (Use your dictionary)

attention _____

_____

connection _____

_____

inspection _____

_____

What am I? Draw me.

I am a shape.
You see me in the mirror.
You see me in water.

I am a _____

Phonics In Context *World Teachers Press*

Read the story.
Underline all the words with 'tion' sounds.

The little red train left the station at 8 o'clock in the morning. He was heading in the direction of the mountains. As he passed through a long tunnel he could see his reflection on the shiny walls. He passed through the middle of a plantation so he would not attract attention. The little red train did not want an inspection because he might have to return to the station. Up and up the mountain, the little train climbed with the friction of the wind in his face. The action of his wheels made a clanging noise as he reached the top of the mountain. The little train stood proud as he looked down over the valley.

Answer these questions.

What time did the train leave the station?

_____

What direction was the train heading?

_____

What could the train see on the wall?

_____

Why didn't the train want an inspection?

_____

Why do you think the train stood 'proud'?

_____

'our' as in pour

Print the missing 'our' sounds.

f__ __ __

p__ __ __   c__ __ __se

c__ __ __t   s__ __ __ce

Put in the missing word.

four   Please _____ me a drink.

pour   Number _____ is my favorite number.

source   If you paddle your canoe around the wrong
            _____, you could get lost.

course   What is the policeman's
            _____ of information?

What is the meaning of: (Use your dictionary)

source _____

_____

course _____

_____

Read the story.
Circle all the words with 'our' sounds.

On the fourth day of each month a course is set for racing. First the riders must put on helmets, goggles, gloves and boots to take the bikes for a test run. Sometimes water is poured on the track to keep the dust down. As the racers race around the course they must take great care not to fall off. Ribbons are given to first, second, third, and fourth place. The fourth place rider only receives a small ribbon as an incentive to try harder next time. All racers enjoy the meet and look forward to the fourth day in each month.

Answer these questions.

On what day does the club

hold their races? _____

What must the racers wear?

_____

Why is the fourth place ribbon smaller?

_____

Why should the racers take care?

_____

Why do you think the racers enjoy the day?

_____

'ey' as in monkey

Print the missing 'ey' sound.

turk_ _   donk_ _

parsl_ _   jock_ _

vall_ _   chimn_ _

monk_ _   mon_ _

all_ _

Choose from the above words to fill in the blanks.

A _____ looks like a small horse.

A _____ swings from tree to tree.

I need _____ to shop with.

The land between two hills is called a _____.

A _____ is a person who rides a horse in a race.

Read the story.
Underline all the words with 'ey' sounds.

One day a monkey and a donkey became friends. The monkey rode on the donkey's back, just like a jockey. He rode through the valley until he came to a dark alley. The donkey stopped and would not go down the alley. The monkey tried very hard to make the donkey move but the donkey would not go down the alley. At the end of the alley, smoke was billowing out of a chimney.

Answer these questions.

What is a valley?

_____

_____

_____

What is a jockey?

_____

_____

Who became friends?

_____

Why do you think the donkey wouldn't move?

_____

_____

'ie' as in thief

Print the missing 'ie' sound.

bel__ __f   p__ __ce

gr__ __f   rel__ __f

bel__ __ve   th__ __f

br__ __f   d__ __sel

shr__ __k   sh__ __ld

pr__ __st   ch__ __f

Choose from the words above to fill in the blanks.

Put a _____ of pie in the oven to heat.

The woman gave a loud _____ when a spider
dropped on her shoulder.

The _____ was caught by the police officer as he
tried to run from the store.

The Indian _____ used his _____ to protect
himself.

Write words which rhyme with:

chief _____

Read the story.
Circle all the words with 'ie' sounds.

The chief of a small Indian village was relieved when a piece of arrow broke as it hit the shield. A shriek was heard for a brief moment as a thief was spotted running off into the bushes. The chief could not believe his eyes. He believed all his people were honest. He was relieved to learn that the thief was not one of his own people. After a brief chase the thief was caught. He was paraded before all the Indians with a priest as a witness. The thief begged to be forgiven and promised he would never steal again.

Answer these questions.

Why wasn't the chief hit by the arrow?

_____

Why did the thief run off into the bushes?

_____

Why do you think the thief was paraded in front of all the Indians?

_____

What kind of a person do you think the thief was?

_____

'o' as in move

Say these words.

move	to do
prove	lose
whose	into
do	who

Choose from the words above to fill in the blanks.

1. One day we are going to _____ to another school.

2. We walked _____ a spider's web. The spider

   had to _____ to another place.

3. I was running behind everyone else. I knew

   I was going to _____ the race.

Write a sentence for:

whose, prove, who

_____

_____

_____

Phonics In Context *World Teachers Press*

Read the story.
Circle all the words with 'o' sounds.

The boy knew he was going to lose the race when he saw that everyone else was in front of him. He began to lose when he fell over a shoe into another lane. He didn't know what to do because he didn't know whose shoe it was. He had to move faster to prove to himself he could do better than last place. He ran faster and faster and proved that he was better than last place by coming fourth.

Answer these questions.

Why did the boy fall over?

_____

_____

Could the boy run fast?

_____

How did he feel about losing the race?

_____

How do you think he felt when he came fourth?

_____

_____

Who do you think the shoe belongs to?

_____

'ey' as in prey

Say these words.

prey	obey
they	survey

Choose from the words above to fill in the blanks

Before you lead a party of explorers you should

_____ the area.

A hawk is a bird of _____.

Animals _____ on weaker animals.

A _____ is a list of questions.

At school you are taught to _____ your parents

and teachers.

Read and draw.

A lion waiting
to prey on deer as
they drink from a
water hole.

Read the story.
Underline all the words with 'ey' sounds.

Many animals prey on other animals. The stronger species prey on the weaker species. For instance, lions prey on deer as they graze. They wait as the deer grazes until it is not suspicious of being watched. The lion surveys the area and when it is the right time the lion will strike and the deer will be killed. The eagle with its excellent eyesight soars through the sky watching below for smaller animals. It preys on rabbits and smaller rodents.

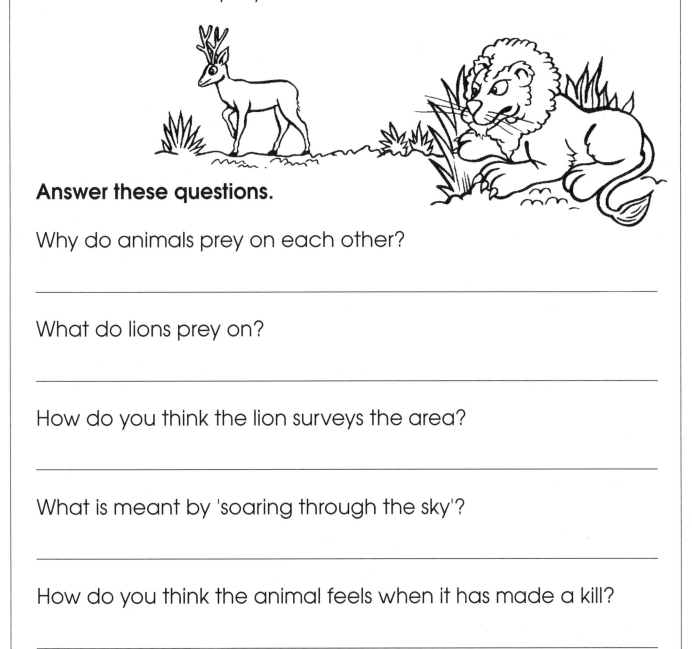

Answer these questions.

Why do animals prey on each other?

_____

What do lions prey on?

_____

How do you think the lion surveys the area?

_____

What is meant by 'soaring through the sky'?

_____

How do you think the animal feels when it has made a kill?

_____

'ain' as in fountain

Print the missing 'ain' sound.
Then rewrite each word.

fount___ ___ ___   _____

capt___ ___ ___   _____

barg___ ___ ___   _____

mount___ ___ ___   _____

cert___ ___ ___   _____

curt___ ___ ___   _____

Use these words in a sentence.

fountain, captain, bargain

_____

_____

_____

Answer 'Yes' or 'No'.

Can you climb a mountain? _____

Is a fountain the same as a chieftain?_____

Can a curtain be made out of fabric? _____

Read the story.
Circle all the words with 'ain' sounds.

The captain of the local football team was certain his team would become fit if they ran up to the top of the mountain. His team ran up the mountain and at the top stood a chieftain. The chieftain had wrapped around him curtain material. On the ground, in front of the chieftain, lay many pieces of curtain material. The captain and his team bought many pieces of curtain material from the chieftain. They got the curtain material for a bargain. Down the mountain they ran.

Answer these questions.

What did the captain want his team

to do? _____

_____

Who stood at the top of the mountain?

_____

Why was the chieftain wrapped in curtain material?

_____

How do you think the team felt when they bought their

bargains? _____

Why do you think the team ran down the mountain?

_____

'igh' as in fright

Print the missing 'igh' sound.
Then rewrite each word.

n__ __ __t   _____

fr__ __ __t   _____

l__ __ __t   _____

th__ __ __   _____

f__ __ __t   _____

s__ __ __   _____

Unscramble these words.

ihgftr _____

lgfhti _____

rtgih _____

hting _____

ghis _____

tshig _____

What part of your body is your 'thigh'? Draw it.

Read the story.
Underline all the words with 'igh' sounds.

Last night Trevor heard a sigh coming from behind a dark bush. He got such a fright he ran right into a fence which he did not see. As he hit the fence a bird in the tree got a fright and it took flight, right across the road to another tree. Trevor ran inside his house and turned the light on so he could see who made the sigh. It was so dark outside he couldn't see who gave him such a fright. He climbed into bed and fell asleep. In the morning he was glad the night was over because he had such a fright the previous night.

Answer these questions.

What was heard last night?

_____

Who heard the sound?

_____

Why did Trevor hit the fence?

_____

Why do you think Trevor went to bed?

_____

Why do you think Trevor was frightened?

_____

'gh' as in "f" and "ph" sounds

Read each word. Sort them into three groups.

rough	four
Stefanie	five
Stephen	tough
trough	elephant
laugh	orphan
alphabet	telephone

Write the meaning for: (Use your dictionary)

trough _____

rough _____

tough _____

graph _____

sphinx _____

Read the story.
Circle all the words with 'gh', 'f' and 'ph' sounds.

Stefanie and Stephen were two orphan children. One day they received a telephone call from an old friend. Their friend wanted to take them to the zoo. They saw an elephant drinking from a trough. The trough had a rough edge and it scratched the elephant's trunk. The elephant's skin was tough so it did not hurt. As Stefanie and Stephen walked past the trough, Stefanie slipped and fell into the trough. Stephen and Stefanie couldn't stop laughing. Stefanie was wet through. Their friend took the two orphan children home.
They had a lovely day.

Answer these questions.

What were the children's names?

_____

_____

What did their friend want to do?

_____

How do you think the trough got the rough edges?

_____

Why do you think the two children laughed?

_____

How do you think the friend felt when Stefanie got wet?

_____

'ous' as in famous

Print the missing 'ous' sound.

seri__ __ __   adventur__ __ __

joy__ __ __   poison__ __ __

fam__ __ __   enorm__ __ __

jeal__ __ __   nerv__ __ __

danger__ __ __

Put in the missing words.

The _____ explorer climbed Mt. Everest.

He felt _____ when he reached the top.

It is very _____ if you get bitten by a _____

snake.

An _____ crocodile swam near the boat, it

made us all very _____.

Write a sentence for:

jealous, adventurous

_____

_____